CREATIVE COLORING

DESIGN ELEMENTS

Art Sherwyn

Table of Contents

Printed in China
ISBN: 0-87192-584-2
10 9 8 7 6 5 4 3 2 1

Preface

Coloring books have always intrigued me. A staple in most households, they could have tremendous potential for awakening the artistic and creative spirit of anyone using them. This coloring book explores the world of abstraction. The pages provide new and interesting ways to look at objects and scenes. Many of the coloring decisions you make can help inspire your own creative process.

Here are a few suggestions to help you explore this experience.

• Work at your own pace. You do not have to finish a picture in one sitting. It's OK to work back and forth among pages.

• Keep some scratch paper close at hand. Work out your designs and color combinations before you put them on the coloring page. Artists think through their sketches.

• Try using crayons, colored pencils, or both. I like the blending ability and surface quality of crayons, but I also like the control and hard edges of the colored pencil.

• Explore beyond the boundaries that I have set. There are no limitations to creativity!

I now invite you to participate in an experience that will be fun, insightful, and rewarding as you color your way to learning more about the world of art.

—Art Sherwyn

Blending Colors

When colors overlap, they often blend. Try your hand at blending colors on this page. Begin with a light color. Then layer a darker color on top of the light one and gently mix the two. Blended colors can add interest and unity to an artwork. Art that has blended colors can express a variety of feelings, such as peace, joy, sadness, or excitement.

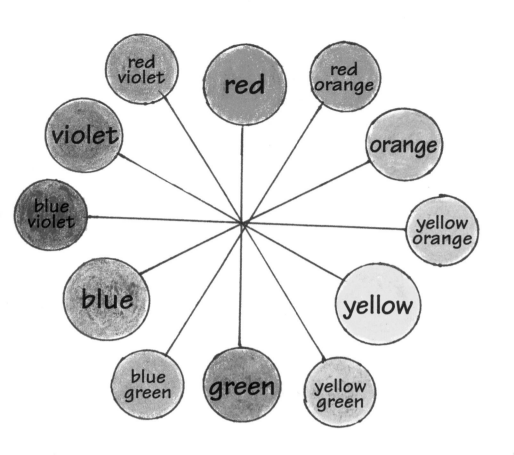

Warm colors, such as red, orange, and yellow, remind us of things and experiences that create warm feelings. The yellows in a campfire or the yellow-orange we see in the sun are examples. Warm colors can also express moods that are happy, bright, and alive.

Warm Colors and Cool Colors

Cool colors, such as blue, green, and violet, remind us of things and experiences that create cool feelings. Think of the blues in a mountain lake and greens of large shade trees. Or think of those winter days when your lips turn blue from the cold. Cool colors can also express "blue" feelings, such as sadness and loneliness.

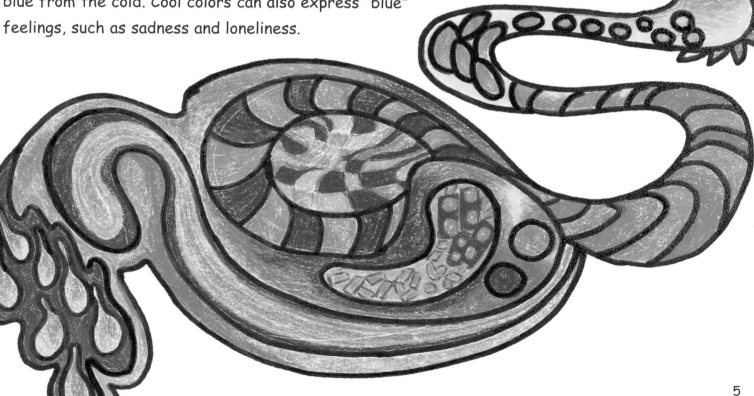

Color this page using only warm colors.

Color this page using only cool colors.

Busy Shapes and Quiet Shapes

In many works of art, some of the shapes are busy and catch your eye. Other shapes are quiet and give your eye a rest. If all the shapes are busy, the viewer will find it hard to see any one of them. The quiet shapes allow the eye to focus on the busy shapes. Part of every picture should speak and part of every painting should listen.

On these two pages, select the shapes that you feel are busy, and color them with warm colors. Select the shapes that you feel are quiet, and color them with cool colors.

Drawing a Design with Busy and Quiet Shapes

Practice creating your own design in the squares provided on page 11. Begin a design by drawing the large shapes first. Most of the large shapes should touch two or more edges of a square. Fill some of the large shapes with small shapes. If you want your design to be busy, add a lot of small shapes. If you want your design to be quiet, draw fewer small shapes and leave more large shapes empty.

To enhance your design, color the busy shapes with warm colors and the quiet shapes with cool colors. Notice how the quiet areas help you focus on the busy areas.

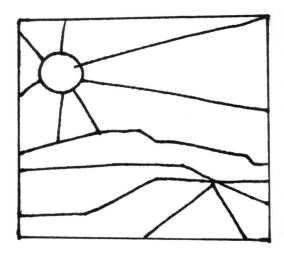

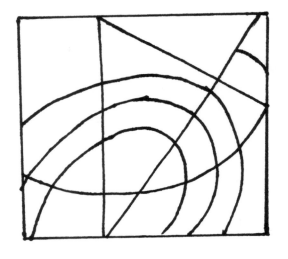

Complementary Colors and Analogous Colors

Complementary colors are opposite one another on the color wheel. For example, red is the complement of green; blue is the complement of orange; and violet is the complement of yellow. When placed next to each other, both colors appear brighter and convey moods that reflect action, liveliness, and excitement. Artists sometimes use complementary colors to create contrast, or strong differences between elements in an artwork.

Analogous colors are next to each other on the color wheel. Red, red-orange, and orange are examples of analogous colors. In a work of art, analogous colors can convey the feelings of rest, peace, and togetherness. Analogous colors can also create a sense of unity in an artwork.

Use contrasting colors to color page 13. Place complementary colors or other contrasting colors next to each other throughout the page.

Drawing a Design for Contrasting Colors

Begin by drawing various combinations of shapes inside a shape. Create your designs in the squares provided on page 15. Use a variety of shapes and sizes to add interest to your design.

Color your design with contrasting colors. Watch your design come alive!

Use analogous colors on page 16. The rainbow can serve as a transition from warm analogous colors to cool analogous colors.

There are many ways to color a shape. Here are some of my own examples. As you color this book, feel free to make up your own combinations.

Layering blended color

Coloring with lines

Line over blended color

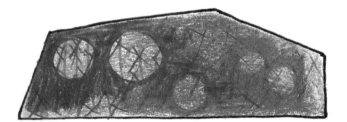

Blocking out

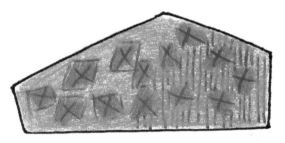

Multiple layering with shape and line

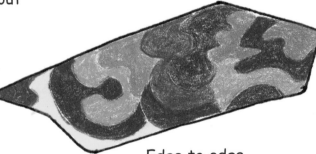

Edge to edge

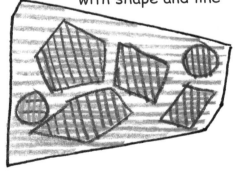

Layering line over blended color

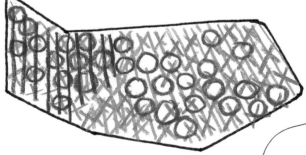

Multiple layers of line

17

Line, Pattern
and Repetition

A **pattern** is a choice of lines, shapes, or colors that are repeated in a planned way. Patterns can be made from just one of the three elements or any combination of them. Color in the patterns on these pages. Then create your own patterns in the empty boxes on page 18.

Once you have created a pattern that you like, you can repeat the pattern itself throughout a larger shape. Experiment with your own patterns and color in the empty shapes.

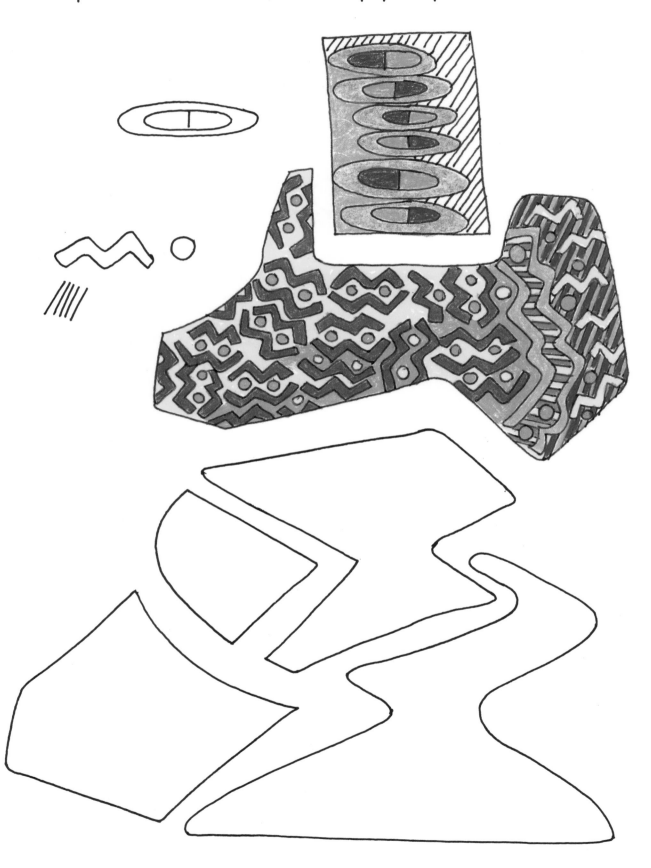

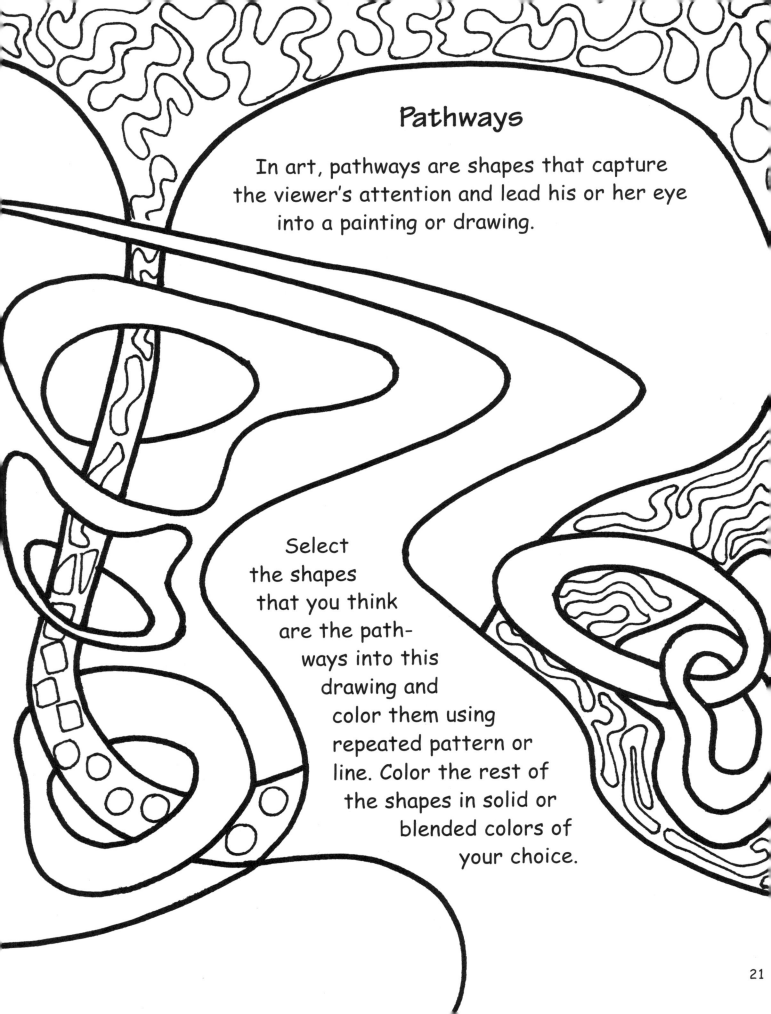

Pathways

In art, pathways are shapes that capture the viewer's attention and lead his or her eye into a painting or drawing.

Select the shapes that you think are the pathways into this drawing and color them using repeated pattern or line. Color the rest of the shapes in solid or blended colors of your choice.

Drawing a Design with Pathways

Create an interesting pathway. You may draw more than one pathway if you wish. To make your pathway more inviting, vary its width and direction. Don't be afraid to experiment.

Next, create a unique, colorful, repetitive design for your pathway. Color the space outside the pathway with solid or blended color. Watch how your pathway lights up and guides your eye around the page!

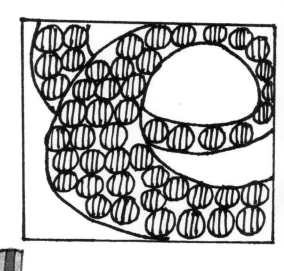

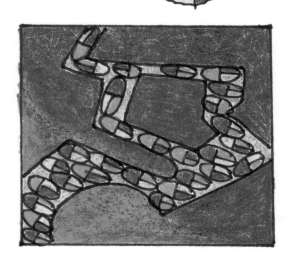

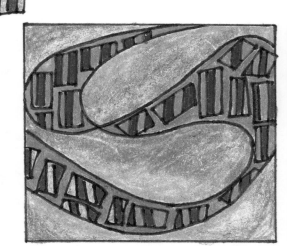

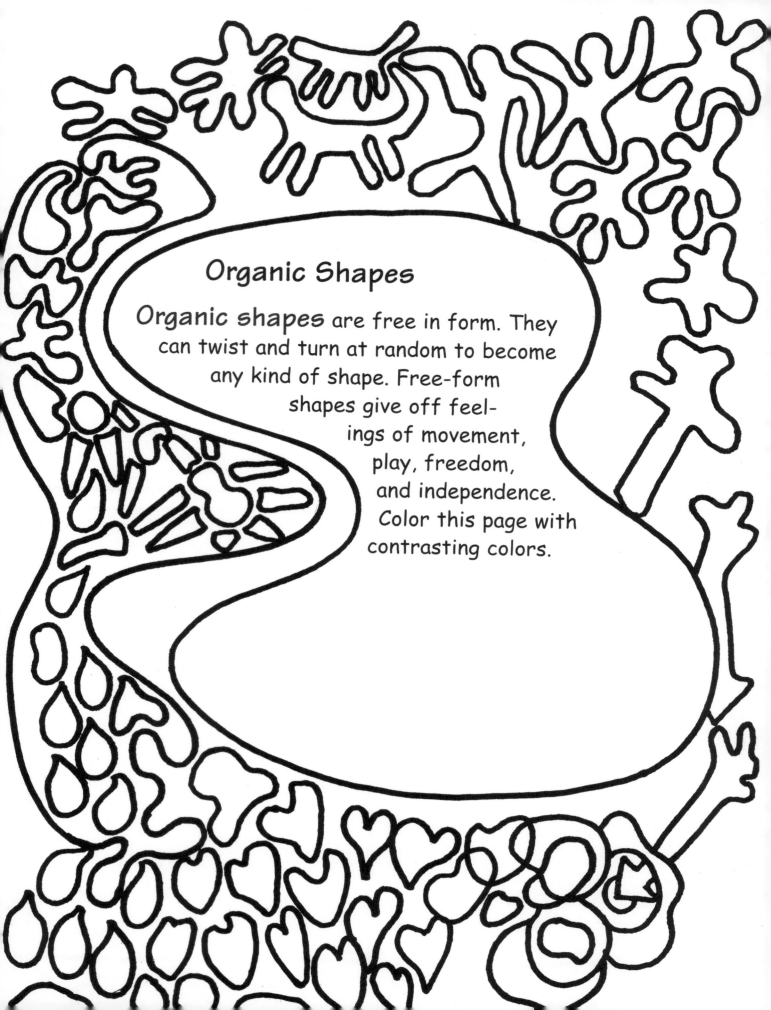

Organic Shapes

Organic shapes are free in form. They can twist and turn at random to become any kind of shape. Free-form shapes give off feelings of movement, play, freedom, and independence. Color this page with contrasting colors.

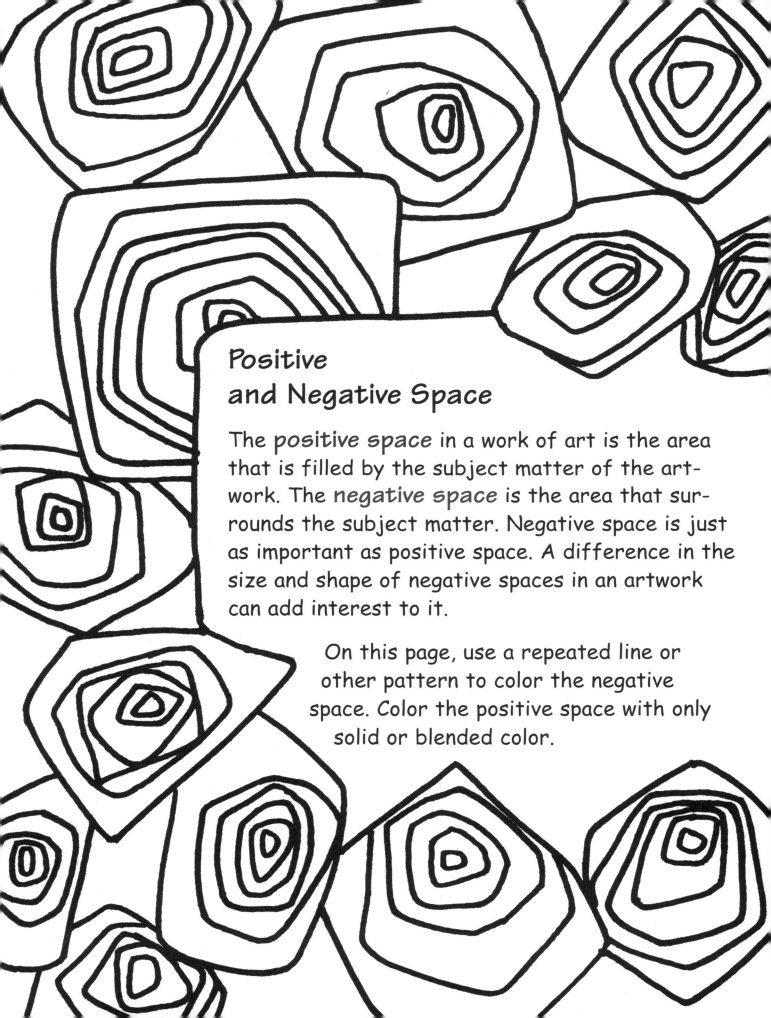

Positive and Negative Space

The positive space in a work of art is the area that is filled by the subject matter of the artwork. The negative space is the area that surrounds the subject matter. Negative space is just as important as positive space. A difference in the size and shape of negative spaces in an artwork can add interest to it.

On this page, use a repeated line or other pattern to color the negative space. Color the positive space with only solid or blended color.

Drawing a Design with Organic Shapes

Begin by drawing three organic shapes in each of the squares provided on page 27. Two of the shapes in each square should touch the edge. The shapes should also overlap each other in one or two areas.

Next, color the positive shapes with solid or blended color. Color the areas that overlap with a line pattern. Color the negative space with a different pattern.

On this page, color the negative space with repeated design.
Color everything else with solid or blended color.

On this page, select three figures that capture your attention the most. Color them with a decorative, repeated pattern. Color the remaining figures in solid or blended color. Finally, color the negative space with solid or blended colors that contrast with the figure colors.

More Shape Concepts

Geometric shapes are universal mathematical shapes that are made from straight lines and angles. They include squares, triangles, octagons, circles, and rectangles. Geometric shapes in a work of art can add stability to its emotional content.

The **focal point** is the area of an artwork that catches the viewer's eye and invites him or her to take a longer look. It is usually a shape or area of shapes that is different from the others.

On these pages, select the shape or area of shapes that you think is the focal point, and color it with a repeated design.

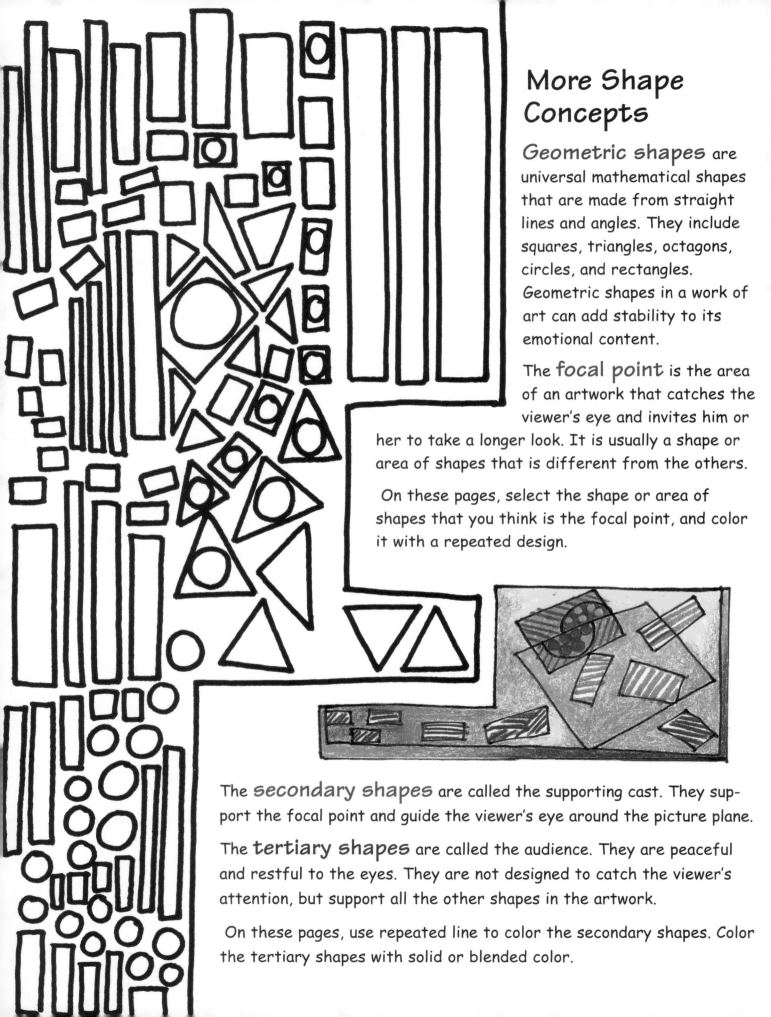

The **secondary shapes** are called the supporting cast. They support the focal point and guide the viewer's eye around the picture plane.

The **tertiary shapes** are called the audience. They are peaceful and restful to the eyes. They are not designed to catch the viewer's attention, but support all the other shapes in the artwork.

On these pages, use repeated line to color the secondary shapes. Color the tertiary shapes with solid or blended color.

Drawing a Design with Geometric Shapes

Draw a series of geometric shapes in the squares provided. Allow some of the shapes to touch or run off the edge of the square. Let some of the shapes overlap to form other shapes.

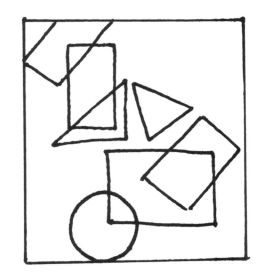

Create a focal point in your drawing. Remember that a focal point captures the viewer's attention. To make the focal point more interesting, add a series of smaller shapes. Add small shapes to some other areas of the drawing to help create unity and guide the viewer's eye to other parts of the design. Be careful not to overdo it, however, or you will take the emphasis away from the focal point.

To enhance your design, color the focal point with a repeated design. Use repeated line to color the secondary shapes. Fill the tertiary shapes with solid or blended color.

Fauvism

In 1898, the style of painting known as Fauvism began in France, when artists Andre Derain and Maurice de Vlaminck met and shared ideas.

Derain rejected the Impressionists' style of painting and chose instead to work with pure color and strong brush-strokes. Other artists who painted in this style include Henri Matisse, Henri Manguin, Raoul Dufy, and Albert Marquet.

André Dérain, *St. Paul's from the Thames*, 1906. Oil on canvas, 39 ¼ x 32 ¼" (99.7 x 82 cm). The Minneapolis Institute of Arts.

In 1905, the group had their first exhibition. The paintings shocked exhibition visitors with their bold and intensely bright colors. To one art critic, the name Les Fauves—the French term for the wild beasts— seemed to fit these artists quite well!

The Fauves painted directly from nature, using brighter-than-expected color. The variety of brushstrokes they used range from broken to solid and calm to energetic. Together, the brushstrokes and colors evoke strong sensations and emotions in viewers.

The Fauvist movement ended in 1908, as its artists started developing their own styles and Cubism began to take hold.

André Dérain, *Portrait of Maurice de Vlaminck*, 1905. Oil on cardboard, 16 ⅛ x 13" (41 x 33 cm). © ARS, New York. Private Collection, Chartres, France.

Maurice de Vlaminck, *The Blue House*, 1906. Oil on canvas, 21 ½ x 25 ½" (54.6 x 64.8 cm). The Minneapolis Institute of Arts.

Color like a Fauvist.

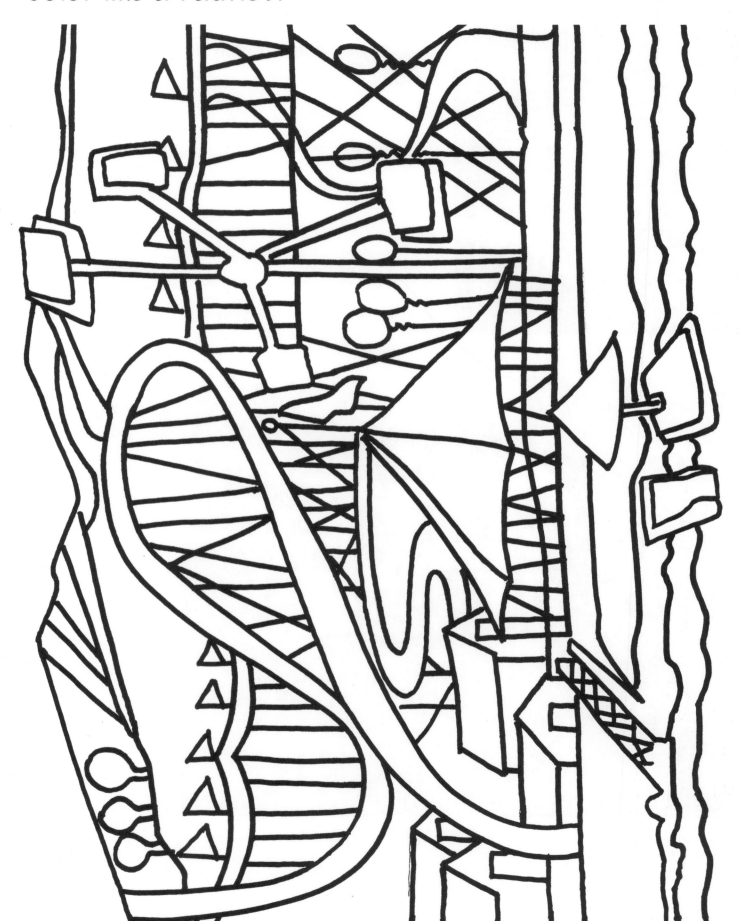

On the pages that follow, use what you have learned to color the drawings any way you wish. Create your own designs in the squares provided. Let your imagination go wild!

On this page, experiment with the different techniques that you have learned.

On this page, try creating a design with warm or cool colors. Where will your focal point be?

What kinds of shapes can you create on this page? How will you color them?

On this page, try a design that uses pattern in some shapes and blended or solid color in other shapes. See if you can create a pathway.

Create your ultimate design on this page.

About the Author

Art Sherwyn became an art teacher quite by accident. Originally hired in 1972 as a high-school coach, with no conscious plans of becoming an art teacher, he was asked by the school to teach arts and crafts during the day. What was once a difficult subject to teach became a lifelong passion. He has since received several awards, including the prestigious American Disney Teacher Award and the awards for National Secondary Art Educator of the Year for the Pacific Region and California High School Art Educator of the Year.

In addition to his career as an art teacher, Sherwyn is a well-known plein-air artist, having painted landscapes throughout California and the United States. He also creates contemporary works of art in his studio. His works have won numerous awards and can be seen in many private collections, exhibits, and museums.

Sherwyn is a lecturer, demonstrator, and motivational speaker, having presented scores of presentations throughout the country. To learn more about Sherwyn and his work, visit his website at www.artsherwyn.com.